Sammy Sun Is Coming Out To Play

Written and created by
Yvonne Fleming

Illustrated by
James Salenga

ISBN 978-0-9955335-0-9

A CIP catalogue record for this book is available from the British Library

www.theweatherbies.co.uk

Sammy Sun is smiling,
As he sits up in his bed,
He rubs his eyes and stretches,
Happy thoughts go through his head.

01

On go Sammy's sunglasses,
And his big, bright, shiny smile,
Then he buckles up his sandals,
'Cause that's just Sammy's style.

He's looking for his friends,
To play some outdoor games,
Pulling on his favourite sunhat,
As he dashes down the lane.

03

He dries up all the puddles,
As he skips and runs along,
Whistling and humming,
His cheerful, happy song.

Sammy sees his friends,
When he gets to Puddle Place,
He shouts out, in a happy voice,
"Let's go have a race!"

Ronny Rain runs over,
And splashes him for fun.
"Splash all you like; I won't cool down!"
Laughs steaming Sammy Sun.

Willy Wind is at the park,
Blowing leaves up in the air,
"Don't do that!" cries Ronny Rain,
"You're messing up my hair!"

All lined up, Flo Snow's in place,
They'll soon be on their way,
Rosie Rainbow shouts to them,
"Wait! I'd like to play!"

08

The friends line up to start the race,
In a straight and tidy row,
Counting all together,
1,2,3 GO!

Willy Wind goes whooshing off,
Running super fast!
Blowing leaves and papers,
As he goes zooming past.

Colin Cloud keeps rolling,
As he spins and turns his wheels,
He keeps on getting faster,
Now he's close on Willy's heels!

Sammy Sun is getting hotter,
His cheeks are glowing bright,
He passes Ronny Rain,
As he runs with all his might.

But no one can beat Willy Wind,
He wins and shouts "Hooray!"
"I'm the fastest Weatherbie,
In the Skytown race today!"

"Oh dear" says Flo Snow, giggling,
"I think that I came last.
My little snowy legs,
Aren't made to run so fast!"

"First or last, it's no big deal,"
Smiles happy Sammy Sun,
"We all joined in, we all ran fast,
And we all had lots of fun."

I hope you and your children enjoy getting to know the Weatherbies as much as I have enjoyed creating them for my two lovely sons, Steven and Shane. They both have their favourite characters and I hope you find your favourites too. I dedicate this book in loving memory of my father James who was always there for me. Thank you dad.
We will always remember you xxxx.

PUBLISHED BY THE WEATHERBIES LIMITED
© COPYRIGHT 2010 THE WEATHERBIES LTD
ALL RIGHTS RESERVED.
WWW.THEWEATHERBIES.CO.UK

MORE CHARACTERS AND STORIES TO COME!
FULL OF FUN AND ADVENTURES FROM
THE WEATHERBIES!

Sammy Sun

Colin Cloud

Ronny Rain

Rosie Rainbow

Willy Wind

Flo Snow

Harry Hail

Tommy Thunder

The Lightning Twins

Barry Star

Mary Moon

www.theweatherbies.co.uk

MATCH THE WEATHERBIES CHARACTER TO THEIR NAME

Ronny Rain

Sammy Sun

Willy Wind

Flo Snow

Colin Cloud

Rosie Rainbow

Barry Star

Harry Hail

Mary Moon

Tommy Thunder

The Lightning Twins